£3.40

Hotspur
BOOK FOR BOYS

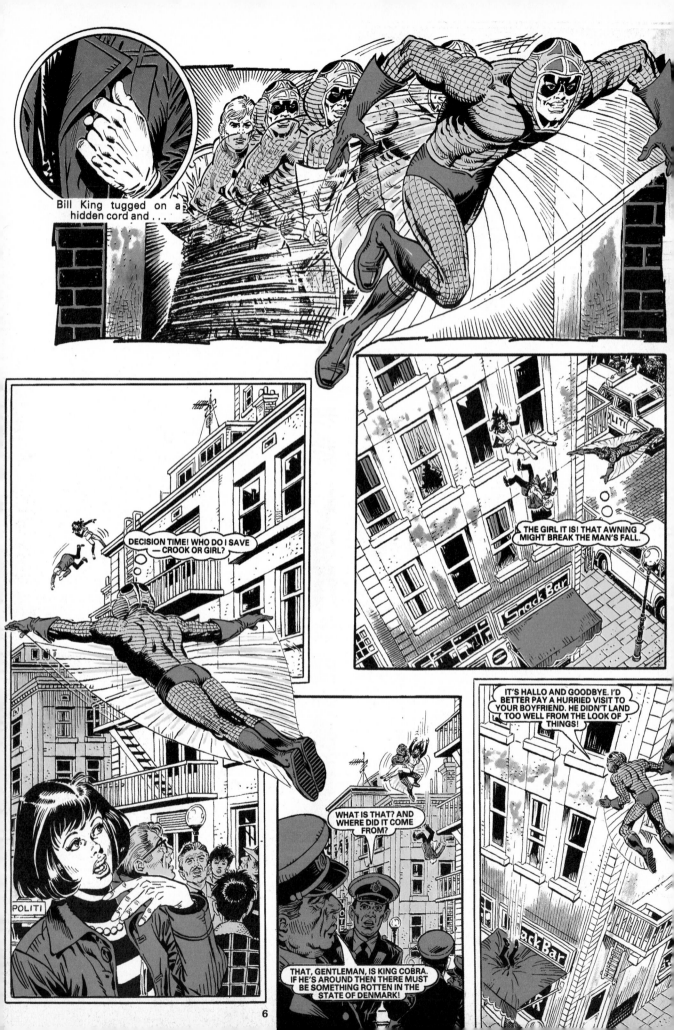

Bill King tugged on a hidden cord and . . .

DECISION TIME! WHO DO I SAVE — CROOK OR GIRL?

THE GIRL IT IS! THAT AWNING MIGHT BREAK THE MAN'S FALL.

IT'S HALLO AND GOODBYE. I'D BETTER PAY A HURRIED VISIT TO YOUR BOYFRIEND. HE DIDN'T LAND TOO WELL FROM THE LOOK OF THINGS!

WHAT IS THAT? AND WHERE DID IT COME FROM?

THAT, GENTLEMAN, IS KING COBRA. IF HE'S AROUND THEN THERE MUST BE SOMETHING ROTTEN IN THE STATE OF DENMARK!

6

THAT DUMPER WITH THE LOAD OF SAND IS HEAVEN-SENT! BUT I'VE ONLY SECONDS TO HANDLE IT!

CAUTION

IT'S WORKING!

WHAT? MY LOAD!!

ALL IN A GOOD CAUSE, PAL...

...YOU'VE JUST SAVED A LADY'S NECK!

WHO WAS THAT?

THAT, MISTER, IS KING COBRA. NOW, IF I HAD HIM ON MY STAFF INSTEAD OF THAT WEAK-KNEED BILL KING...

WELL, WELL! SO YOU'RE STILL IN ONE PIECE, AND NOT SO MUCH YELLOW AS BLACK AND BLUE — I HOPE!

OKAY, DON'T RUB IT IN. COULDN'T SEE WHAT ELSE TO DO... YOU COULD HAVE DONE THE SAME.

On the flight to Copenhagen...

YOU REALISE, OF COURSE, THAT THE BRAKE FAILURE WAS NO ACCIDENT. I'M CLOSER TO A LINK IN THIS DRUG RACKET THAN I REALISED.

OH, COME ON, KING! IF YOU THINK YOU CAN SCARE ME OFF BY OVER DRAMATISING THIS STORY—

IT CAN ONLY MEAN I'M ON TO SOMETHING — AND IT COULD BE THAT TRIGGER-HAPPY COP. MAYBE HE WAS TOLD TO GET HANSEN BEFORE HE COULD TALK.

HO-HUM! ANYTHING BUT ADMIT THAT THE TOUGH, HUSKY MALE CAN'T SERVICE HIS OWN CAR PROPERLY!

CONTINUED ON PAGE 49.

11

13

14

YOU'RE DOING REAL GOOD, SPORT. NOW ALL YOU GOT TO DO IS TAKE ME OVER TO FRANCE AND I'LL THANK YOU WITH A WAD OF THE FOLDING STUFF IN THIS BAG.

THAT AIN'T POSSIBLE WITH THE JUICE WE'VE GOT IN THE TANK. WE'D RUN DRY HALFWAY.

SPORT, YOU JUST SAID THE WRONG THING.

IT'S THE TRUTH. I WAS OFF TO FETCH PETROL WHEN YOU SHOWED UP.

IZZAT SO! ALL RIGHT, SO WE GO BACK AND YOU GET THAT GAS.

A LOOP IN THE OTHER END OF THIS NYLON AND MAYBE — WELL, JUST MAYBE.

I WON'T BE LONG, MISTER.

YOU CAN COUNT ON THAT, KID, 'CAUSE I'M COMING WITH YOU! ANY TRICKS FROM YOU OR YOUR OLD MAN AND I START SHOOTING.

THIS JERRICAN'S HEAVY, MISTER. YOU'D BETTER HELP ME.

YEAH, KID, I'M NICE THAT WAY — AND I'LL STILL HAVE A HAND FREE FOR MY SHOOTER.

GOT IT! NOW ALL I HAVE TO DO IS PAY OUT THE LINE WITHOUT HIM NOTICING.

15

Charlie "stumbled" . . .

GOT IT, SPORT! NOW GET THIS TUB MOVING.

OOPS! SORRY, MISTER.

WATCH IT, KID.

As the boat moved out, a nylon line grew taut . . .

EH! WHAT THE —

RH.72

AAAAAAAAAAAAAAH!

LUMME! IT WORKED.

SON, I HAVE TO ADMIT YOU SHOW PROMISE AS A FISHERMAN. THAT KNOT CERTAINLY HELD! PERHAPS WE SHOULD WEIGH THIS 'UN BEFORE WE HAND HIM OVER TO THE POLICE.

THE END

16

CROCODILE McGHEE

AAHR, TOMMY, THERE'S CROCS IN THAT CREEK!

SORRY, MATT!

Crocodile Matt McGhee was playing football with his mates during the lunch break at the quarry in Woolongong, Australia . . .

LOOK OUT, MATT! CROCODILE!

Matt's wrist had been broken in a football match . . .

HE'S GOIN' FOR OUR BALL!

KLUNK!

THIS PLASTER'S GOT ITS USES!

21

23

On Saturday United were at home to Braxton Roberts who were fifth bottom of the league. Seventeen-year-old Bobby Young was getting his first game for United . . .

NO NEED TO BE NERVY, SON! YOU'RE A THOUSAND TIMES BETTER'N THE REST OF OUR LOT.

G . . .GEE, THANKS, CROCODILE.

THE AUSSIE THINKS HE'S TOUGH BUT HE AIN'T MET HACKER YET!

COR, TIE ME KANGAROO DOWN! HE TACKLES LIKE ME MATES BACK IN AUSTRALIA. MAKES ME FEEL AT HOME!

THAT SHOWED 'IM! HACKER'S THE DIRTIEST PLAYER IN THE DIVISION!

TO YOU, ANDY!

GOOD BALL, HACKER!

YEEEEES! ONE NIL!

STONE THE CROWS. I DIDN'T BECOME MANAGER TO GET BEATEN IN MY FIRST GAME!

CONTINUED ON PAGE 89.

THE MUD PLUGGERS

Moto cross is muddy and dangerous but can provide lots of thrills for riders and spectators alike.

The one thing no-one wants to see! Two bikes collide during a close race.

"I think they went that-a-way!" It looks like this rider has lost the rest of the pack.

Neck and neck over a bump, these two riders battle it out.

Number twenty-nine takes an early lead as the riders take the first bend.

That night in a dingy cellar . . .

WHAT MADE YOU SAVE ME, JACK?

THIS, MR FRY . . . PLUS I ALWAYS STRONGLY SUSPECTED YOU WERE INNOCENT!

GHOST WALKS?

AT COLLBY HALL, SIR PERCY'S PLACE. I DON'T BELIEVE IN GHOSTS, MR FRY. THERE'S A NEW OWNER AT COLLBY HALL. I'D BE VERY INTERESTED TO HAVE A LOOK AT HIM . . . AND THE GHOST!

Next day . . .

I'D LIKE TO TAKE SOME OF MY ANNUAL HOLIDAYS, SERGEANT DREW.

HOLIDAYS, JACKSON? HMM . . . VERY WELL. YOUR WORK ISN'T AS IMPORTANT AS REAL SLEUTHING.

That night John Jackson booked in at a little country inn near Collby Hall . . .

YOUR ROOM, SIR.

THANK YOU. I'LL HAVE AN EARLY NIGHT.

Had the maid looked in an hour later, she would have been astonished . . .

TIME FOR SOME GHOST HUNTING!

. . . mild-mannered John Jackson was none other than Spring-Heeled Jack!

COLLBY HALL! MY EASIEST WAY IN WILL BE FROM THE ROOF!

BONG! BONG! BONG!

I TOLD YOU I WANTED THAT TERRIBLE BONGING STOPPED, GREER!

NO ONE CAN STOP IT, SIR. I TRIED. THE CLOCK ALWAYS CHIMES WHEN THE GHOST WALKS.

. . . IT ALWAYS INDICATES A DEATH. THE GHOST WALKED WHEN SIR PERCY DIED.

STUFF AND NONSENSE!

Suddenly . . .

AAAAAAH!

Mervin Plank, the murdered Sir Percy's cousin, was the new owner of the Hall and Silas Greer was his bailiff.

But . . .

IT . . . IT'S GONE! THERE'S NOTHING THERE!

HEART TROUBLE . . . GOT TO TAKE MY MEDICINE!

YOU SAVED MY LIFE, SPRING-HEELED JACK. A MOMENT LATER AND THE GHOST WOULD HAVE GOT ME.

I DID NOTHING. IT JUST FADED AWAY.

I'D LIKE YOU TO STAY FOR A WHILE, JACK, AS MY BODYGUARD.

BUT, SIR, THIS MAN IS WANTED BY THE POLICE!

Meanwhile . . .

FROM THE DESCRIPTION I'VE BEEN GIVEN THAT'S WHAT YOUR SPRING-HEELED JACK PROBABLY LOOKS LIKE.

HMM . . . REMINDS ME OF SOMEONE . . .

SIR, FROM THE BAILIFF AT COLBY HALL. FELT IT HIS DUTY TO LET US KNOW — SPRING-HEELED JACK'S STAYING THERE!

VERY PUBLIC SPIRITED, LET'S GO!

Jack was continuing his investigations at Collby Hall . . .

WHAT'S IN HERE, MR GREER?

IT'S MY DARK ROOM.

AH, SO YOU'RE INTERESTED IN THE NEW ART OF PHOTOGRAPHY.

YES, BUT I DOUBT IF JUST ANYBODY WOULD UNDERSTAND IT. YOU NEED BRAINS FOR THAT.

That evening . . .

THE . . . THE GHOST AGAIN!

DON'T WORRY, SIR. I CAN MAKE YOUR GHOST DISAPPEAR AND REAPPEAR AT WILL!

B . . . BUT . . .

N . . . NO, DON'T SHOOT!

OH, NO, YOU DON'T, GREER!

AAAAGHN!

Just then . . .

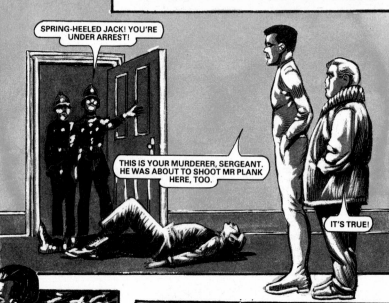

SPRING-HEELED JACK! YOU'RE UNDER ARREST!

THIS IS YOUR MURDERER, SERGEANT. HE WAS ABOUT TO SHOOT MR PLANK HERE, TOO.

IT'S TRUE!

I'D BEST BE GOING, SERGEANT! GLAD TO HAVE HELPED OUT AGAIN.

HOI, COME BACK! I AIN'T FINISHED WITH YOU!

IT'S JUST DAWNED ON ME WHO JACK LOOKS LIKE . . . JOHN JACKSON! BUT NEVER IN A MILLION YEARS COULD I IMAGINE THAT MILKSOP BOUNDING AROUND LIKE JACK!

The End

The COONSKIN GRENADIER

Due to an ancient warrant Zeb Flood from the Great Smokey mountains in Carolina was an honorary colonel in the Royal Grenadiers during the Second World War. Now as the Grenadiers advanced through Germany they came under fire . . .

In Zeb's jeep were Sergeant Major Michin and Zeb's two pets — Alexander the ape and Lightning the hound . . .

SARN'T MAJOR, AIN'T IT SURELY KIND OF COLONEL JODDLE TO LET US RIDE POINT EACH DAY.

URH — OH YES, HE'S MUCH TOO GOOD TO US.

Potomac Barracks in London . . .

THE LATEST FROM THIRD BATTALION, SIR JOHN. ADVANCING THROUGH BAVARIAN ALPS AGAINST ISOLATED POCKETS OF RESISTANCE.

WHAT OF OUR HONORARY COLONEL? HAS ANYTHING HAPPENED TO HIM YET LIKE — ER, PERISH THE THOUGHT — BEING KILLED OR EVEN JUST WOUNDED?

33

34

A shot rang out . . .

TOO LATE! IT IS OVER!

HONORARY COLONEL FLOOD PERISHED IN A GALLANT CHARGE AGAINST THE ENEMY. I SHALL EVEN PUT HIM IN FOR A DECORATION.

THAT'S NICE OF YOU, SIR. PERHAPS I COULD START BACK TOMORROW WITH THE REPORT FOR SIR JOHN.

GENTLEMEN, I MISSED. JUST SHOT A COUPLE OF HOLES IN THE ROOF. FACT IS THAT DOING THE DECENT THING DIDN'T SEEM NOHOW RIGHT AND PROPER.

HUM! DEUCED INCONSIDERATE. AWKWARD TOO.

SIR, HONOUR MAY BE REDEEMED BY UNDERTAKING A HOPELESS MISSION. FLOOD COULD TACKLE THAT RESISTANCE UP ON THE PASS.

AW SHUCKS, COLONEL, I'LL BE TICKLED PINK TO HANDLE THAT LITTLE CHORE.

SARN'T-MAJOR — I KNOWS HOW YOU IS ALWAYS ITCHING FOR ACTION AND YOU ARE WELCOME TO COME ALONG.

HONORARY COLONEL, THIS TIME I'LL FORCE MYSELF TO HOLD BACK AND LEAVE THE GLORY TO YOU.

ALL QUIET SINCE DUSK — WELL, SORT OF! NO FIRING, BUT THERE'S A LOT OF SINGING BEEN GOING ON UP THERE.

I'D BEST GO SEE WHAT'S HAPPENING!

OUR BEST CHANCE IS TO GO UP THOSE HIGH ALPS.

THANKS, ALEXANDER! THOSE CANNON DOWN THERE MUST BE WHAT FIRED ON US. JUST ONE SENTRY, HUH!

THAT THERE STAIRHEAD LOOKS LIKE OUR WAY IN.

I HEAR FOLKS IN THERE, BOYS — ONLY THEY ARE NOT SINGING, JUST SNORING.

NOW I KNOW WHAT THEY MEAN BY OLD SOLDIERS. THIS BUNCH SURE IS LONG IN ANY TEETH THEY GOT LEFT.

ACH WAS — A MONKEY IN UNIFORM.

ACHTUNG! TO ARMS!

PARDON US, GENTS! WE ARE JUST LEAVING!

DEATH TO THE ENGLANDER!

COMRADES — WAIT! THERE IS A MONKEY IN ENGLISH UNIFORM, HIS CAP BEARING A BADGE KNOWN TO US ALL. LOOK! SEE FOR YOURSELVES!

FURRY ONE, WHO ARE YOU?

ZEBADIAH FLOOD, GENTS — HONORARY COLONEL OF THE BRITISH ROYAL GRENADIERS.

SIR, WE SALUTE YOU! WE, THE PENSIONERS OF SCHLOSS FRANKEN, LAST OF THE BLACK EAGLES! NOW YOU SHALL SEE HOW WE HAVE BEEN LOYAL TO OUR TRUST.

THE MESS SILVER OF THE ROYAL GRENADIERS IN OUR KEEPING SINCE OUR REGIMENTS FOUGHT SIDE BY SIDE IN THAT WAR AGAINST THE AMERICAN COLONISTS.

IT'S BEEN QUIET UP THERE ALL NIGHT, SIR. NOTHING HAS BEEN HEARD FROM HONORARY COLONEL FLOOD.

WE MAY ASSUME THE POOR FELLOW IS FINISHED. WELL, GET ON WITH IT. A FEW ROUNDS FROM THE ARMOURED CAR AND THEN RUSH THE PLACE.

SHOT ONE!

I WAS FORGETTING. THAT WILL BE OUR BOYS KNOCKING TO COME IN.

THEN WE MUST LEAVE YOU. THE LAST OF THE BLACK EAGLES GO OUT TO THEIR FINAL BATTLE.

Later —

GEE, SARGE, NO WONDER ONE OF THOSE TWO SHIPS DISAPPEARED FROM OUR LONG RANGE SCREENS!

The police interceptor was crewed by Sergeant Sixty of the Galactic Police and his assistant Patrolman Ben Bateman.

THE OTHER'S GONE TOO! PROBABLY HEADING FOR SCUM CITY!

LOOK! THERE'S SOMEBODY STILL ALIVE!

INCREDIBLE!

THANK YOU, YOUNG MAN!

MY PLEASURE, SIR. YOU'LL BE ABLE TO TELL US WHAT HAPPENED.

YOU MUST EXCUSE ME. MY ORDER FORBIDS ME REVEALING MY FEATURES. THE LEADER WAS A GIANT BEARDED MAN.

THE PIRATE MORGA! THREE OTHER SHIPS HAVE BEEN DESTROYED IN SIMILAR CIRCUMSTANCES BUT THIS IS THE FIRST TIME THERE HAS BEEN A SURVIVOR TO TELL US WHAT HAPPENED.

JUST ONE THING, THOUGH, SIR? HOW COULD YOU SURVIVE OUT THERE WITHOUT A SPACESUIT?

MY SPECIAL GENES, SERGEANT. I'M FROM A FAR PLANET! I CAN SURVIVE MOST CLIMES AND TEMPERATURES.

Sixty landed the monk at Gorthur . . .

GOODBYE AND THANK YOU! I SHALL BE AT THE MONASTERY.

WEIRD CHARACTER. NOT INJURED AT ALL.

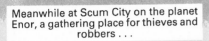

Meanwhile at Scum City on the planet Enor, a gathering place for thieves and robbers . . .

MORE WINE! ROBBING IS THIRSTY WORK!

YOUR HAND, MORGA . . .

MORGA IS BACK!

ODS BODS! WHAT THE . . ?

A day or two later . . .

WE'RE TAKING A CHANCE COMING TO SCUM CITY, SARGE.

IT'S OUR DUTY, BEN. WE MUST BRING MORGA TO BOOK. AND THE WORD IS, HE'S HERE.

IT'S THAT RAT SIXTY. COME TO ARREST SOMEONE!

LET'S HAVE SOME SPORT!

KEEP BACK — OR I'LL SHOOT TO KILL!

THEY CAN'T KILL US ALL! GET THEM!

45

Sixty had previously saved Louis' life!

THE . . . THE SKIN!

NO!

Meanwhile back on Gorthur . . .

LANI ZAVEREZ! SHE'S SAID TO BE THE MOST BEAUTIFUL CREATURE IN ALL THE UNIVERSE. I HATE BEAUTY! I MUST DESTROY IT!

That night there was to be a fancy dress ball . . .

MY COSTUME IS MOST APPROPRIATE!

MAY I HAVE THE HONOUR, MISS ZAVEREZ?

BEAT IT! HER CARD IS FILLED.

THEN MAY I JUST SHAKE HANDS?

THANK YOU.

IT IS DONE . . . THE HANDSHAKE OF DEATH. THERE ARE ENOUGH VENTS IN THE GLOVES FOR HER TO TOUCH MY BONES!

THE MORE I SHAKE HANDS WITH — THE MORE THEY WILL REMEMBER ME!

He left early next morning . . .

SCUM CITY, FULL OF WICKEDNESS AND EVIL. THAT IS THE PLACE FOR ME!

47

Sixty had taken Ben to hospital . . .

ANOTHER ONE! THAT MAKES EIGHT INCLUDING LANI ZAVEREZ, THE MOVIE STAR. SOME KIND OF PLAGUE. IT'S PASSED ON BY A MAN WEARING A SKULL TYPE MASK AND A CAVALIER COSTUME. ALL THE VICTIMS SHOOK HANDS WITH HIM.

BEN DIDN'T — OR MORGA! WE MUST FIND HIM THOUGH! I'LL ASK AROUND.

I HIRED THE CAVALIER COSTUME TO A MONK IN A BLACK ROBE. HE HASN'T BROUGHT IT BACK EITHER!

WAIT A MINUTE! THAT'S WHAT MORGA MUST HAVE BEEN TRYING TO SAY — BLACK MONK, NOT BLACK PLAGUE. THE MONK WAS ON THE SHIP MORGA ROBBED AND BEN RESCUED HIM! IT'S OUR WEIRD FRIEND!

IT REMINDS ME OF AN OLD MYTH ABOUT A DEATH MAN FROM OUTER SPACE! A MAN WHO LIVES THROUGH CENTURIES AND METES OUT DEATH BY A MERE TOUCH!

Sirami Gutra knew all of the old legends and myths . . .

YOU ARE CORRECT, SERGEANT. DEATH MAN IS ON THE PROWL. ONLY ONE THING CAN STOP HIM AND SAVE YOUR FRIENDS. THE JUICE OF THE RARE HALOP PLANT FOUND ONLY ON ZUR!

THEN THAT'S WHERE I MUST GO!

Sixty set out for Zur . . .

THE PLANT IS ON ZUR! BUT I MUST FIRST PASS THROUGH THE DANGEROUS AIR SPACE OF THE GYROTHRONS — WHO SLAUGHTER ALL FOREIGNERS!

ALIEN CRAFT AHEAD! INTERCEPT — AND KILL!

CONTINUED ON PAGE 10

WH-WHAT IS GOING ON?

BACK AGAIN, HUH, KING? WHEN I HEARD AN ENGLISHMAN HAD BEEN CLOBBERED OUTSIDE A COPENHAGEN HOTEL, I JUST KNEW IT HAD TO BE YOU. STILL SNIFFING AROUND THAT DRUG STORY?

NEVER MIND THAT, BRAND. WHERE'S MY BOSS?

THAT WOMAN WHO WAS SNATCHED WAS YOUR BOSS?

YEH! ANYONE GET A MAKE ON THE CAR?

IT HAPPENED FAST, KING. PEOPLE WHO SPOTTED IT WEREN'T EVEN SURE IT WAS A SNATCH. DO YOU THINK IT MIGHT BE CONNECTED WITH —?

OF COURSE IT IS, BRAND! I HAVE TO TALK TO BECK — THAT COP WHO SHOT HANSEN. IT'S OUR ONLY LEAD.

NO WAY! HE'S BEEN SUSPENDED PENDING INVESTIGATION. NO ONE TALKS TO HIM. GET UP TO YOUR ROOM AND LIE DOWN!

I'VE GOT TO SEE BECK. HE'S MY ONLY CLUE!

I'LL FOLLOW BRAND. HE'LL LEAD ME TO BECK!

THERE CAN BE ONLY ONE REASON FOR STOPPING OUT HERE IN THE MIDDLE OF NOWHERE! THEY'VE HIDDEN BECK ON THAT HOUSEBOAT!

GOOD OF THE COPS TO HIDE BECK ON A HOUSEBOAT. NOW I CAN TAKE A LITTLE CRUISE WITH HIM.

THE BOAT'S BROKEN LOOSE!

CUT LOOSE MORE LIKELY!

WHAT THE —? BECK! THEY GOT TO HIM FIRST! BUT AT LEAST HE'S STILL ALIVE!

MMMMPH! GRRNNNNNGH!

A BOMB! THEY — THEY'VE PLANTED A BOMB! SET FOR MIDNIGHT! IN THE LOCKER! GET IT!

THAT GIVES US JUST TWENTY SECONDS TO TALK, BECK. SO TALK FAST! WHO IS BEHIND THE DANISH CONNECTION AND WHERE DO I FIND HIM?

I — I DUNNO THE BIG MAN — BUT THE HQ WAS AT HANSEN'S STOCK-ROOMS! NOW GET US OUT OF HERE!

TOO BAD — WHOEVER YOU ARE! YOU'RE STAYING!

WHAT — YEEARGH!

STILL TEN SECONDS TO GO, BECK. WHERE HAVE THEY TAKEN THE WOMAN?

WOMAN? I — I DON'T KNOW ANYTHING ABOUT A WOMAN.

OKAY, I THINK YOU'RE TELLING THE TRUTH! LET'S GO!

BEHIND YOU, BECK! LOOK OUT!

THAT OLD ONE WON'T WORK, MISTER! SO LONG!

AAAARGH!

TIME'S UP! TOO LATE TO HELP HIM NOW!

AND ONLY JUST IN THE NICK OF TIME!

Meanwhile . . .

MAYBE WE OUGHT TO JUST KILL HER! THIS AIN'T GONNA WORK, BOSS. THERE'S STILL NO REPLY FROM KING'S ROOM.

KEEP TRYING! IF KING WANTS TO SAVE THIS BIRD, WE CAN CALL HIM OFF THE INVESTIGATION. HE TOES THE LINE — OR SHE DIES! THAT'S WHAT WE'LL TELL HIM ANYWAY!

ONCE THE OTHER TWO HAVE FIRED HANSEN'S STOCK-ROOMS AND KING IS SILENCED, THE PRESSURE'S OFF. THEN WE CAN ALL RELAX!

WELL, THERE GOES MY ONLY LEAD. STILL NO CLUES AS TO WHERE THAT KERRIGAN WOMAN IS!

GOT TO CATCH HER!

YOU SEEM TO MAKE A HABIT OF GETTING INTO STICKY SITUATIONS, LADY!

YOU AGAIN! ARE YOU MY PERSONAL GUARDIAN ANGEL?

THERE'S NOTHING PERSONAL IN IT, LADY!

I EVEN RESCUE SCUM LIKE THIS. I WANT HIM TO TALK—

AA-AH! HE'S FALLEN!

ANOTHER LEAD LOST!

HEY! WAIT!

I'M OFF TO SEE IF YOUR COLLEAGUE IS ALL RIGHT. HE WAS WOUNDED UP THERE TRYING TO SAVE YOUR LIFE!

A few minutes and a bit of bandaging later . . .

ER — HI — THAT FLYING SNAKE GUY TOLD ME I'D FIND YOU HERE. YOU OKAY?

YES — NO THANKS TO YOU! MEANWHILE . . . I HAVE FOUND ANOTHER LITTLE CLUE!

CLASSICAL RECORD CO.

THE CLASSICAL MOB AGAIN! THIS HIGH-BROW OUTFIT IS TIED IN IN SOME WAY.

QUITE! AND WE ARE GOING TO DO ALL WE CAN TO EARN THAT REWARD FOR INTERNATIONAL NEWS GROUP, MR KING! SO LET'S GET OUT ON THE ROAD AND START LOOKING!

Next morning . . .

READ THAT! SIR HENRY PACKHAM DEPLORES THAT ONE OF HIS INTERNATIONAL DISTRIBUTION AGENCIES SHOULD HAVE BEEN USED AS A FRONT FOR A DRUG OPERATION . . .

AND HE DEMANDS THAT INTERPOL ACT AT ONCE TO CLEAN UP THE MESS. HE EVEN OFFERS A SUBSTANTIAL REWARD FOR ANY INDIVIDUAL OR GROUP THAT CAN HELP IN RUNNING THE RING-LEADERS TO EARTH!

WE'RE WASTING OUR TIME HERE, LADY. THE DANISH CONNECTION IS BLOWN SKY HIGH. YOU'D BETTER PACK YOUR BAGS . . .

ARE YOU QUITE SURE THERE'S NO POST FOR MR BILL KING? NOTHING BEEN FORWARDED FROM LONDON?

QUITE SURE, MS KERRIGAN! NOTHING AT ALL!

WHAT?

OH — ER HI, KING. YOU READY —?

WHAT IS SHE UP TO NOW?

CONTINUED ON PAGE 81.

58

THE BIG PALOOKA

As they advanced through Italy in 1944, a battalion of American Rangers did not know what to make of Sergeant Jim Ransom, a British Commando attached to the unit . . .

THE WAY I SEE IT THE CAPTAIN ASKED FOR A PRISONER AND WE GOT THESE TWO KRAUT SENTRIES.

PRIVATE SOLDIERS CAN'T GIVE MUCH INFORMATION, SIR. WITH RESPECT, I AM SURE WE CAN DO BETTER. I'LL BE BACK SOON!

SERGEANT, I CAN NEVER FIGURE OUT IF THAT BIG PALOOKA REALLY IS AS DUMB AS HE MAKES OUT.

LOOTENANT, NO GUY COULD BE THAT DUMB.

BRING UP THE WATER WAGON! SCHNELL! SCHNELL! ACH, HOW COULD THIS HAPPEN? WHERE ARE THE SENTRIES?

Minutes later Jim Ransom was back . . .

WHAT HAVE YOU GOT THERE?

A BETTER CLASS OF PRISONER, SIR. I SUGGEST WE NOW WITHDRAW — RAPIDLY!

Two hours later at Ranger H.Q. . . . .

PATROL'S COMING IN, CAPTAIN.

THEY'RE LATE! URH! NOW I CAN TELL THAT BIG LIMEY PALOOKA HIS OUTFIT WANTS HIM BACK.

HUH! WHAT KIND OF PRISONER IS THIS?

A GERMAN KIND, SIR. HE'S WHAT THEY CALL A GENERALMAJOR — A MAJOR-GENERAL IN OUR ARMY!

YOU'LL FEEL MUCH MORE COSY IN YOUR UNIFORM, GENERALMAJOR, SIR.

I'LL BE DURNED.

Next morning . . .

YOU'LL BE DOING US A SERVICE IF YOU DROP THE KRAUT AT CORPS HEADQUARTERS ON THE WAY BACK TO YOUR OUTFIT. WE'RE NOT EQUIPPED TO HANDLE SUCH HEAVY BRASS.

YOU LIMEYS SURE HAVE HEAVY GEAR.

THAT IS MAINLY A FEW SOUVENIRS PICKED UP DURING MY TIME WITH YOUR MOB.

I HAVE NOTHING AGAINST THAT BIG PALOOKA, BUT I'LL ADMIT TO FEELING A MITE EASIER IN MIND NOW HE'S HEADING BACK TO HIS OWN KIND.

SAME HERE, CAPTAIN. THE WAR SEEMS TO GET KIND OF UNHEALTHY WHEN HE MIXES IN IT.

Half an hour later . . .

LOOKS LIKE A TRAFFIC JAM.

KEEP AN EYE ON THE GENERALMAJOR WHILE I TAKE A LOOK.

ARE YOU SAYING A BUNCH OF DESERTERS AND SUCHLIKE RIFF-RAFF CAN HOLD UP THE U.S. ARMY?

THAT OLD BARRACKS HOLDS SOME WILD PRISONERS WHO HAVE RIOTED AND TAKEN ARMS AND HOSTAGES. THEY ARE FIRING ON ANYTHING THAT MOVES.

HMM, I'LL NEED SOME EQUIPMENT!

KEEP WATCHING THE GENERALMAJOR. I AM GOING FOR A WALK.

DON'T MIND ME, BLOKES! YOU JUST CARRY ON WITH WHAT YOU'RE DOING.

HUH — WHAT? HEY, YOU COME BACK HERE.

THE BARRACK WALL SHOULD KEEP ME OUT OF SIGHT OF THOSE CHAPS INSIDE UNTIL I REACH THE MAIN GATE.

HULLOA THERE! DO NOT SHOOT! I AM COMING FOR A TALK!

DO I BLAST HIM?

NO, THAT'S A LIMEY! HE'LL MAKE ANOTHER HOSTAGE FOR BIG MAC.

LIMEY, COME RIGHT ON IN.

YOU FRISK HIM, SLIM! MAYBE HE'S BRUNG US A CAKE IN THAT PACK.

GENTS, THIS ITEM IN MY FIST IS A HAND GRENADE FROM WHICH I AM TAKING OUT THE PIN. NOW I AM ASKING YOU BOTH TO PUT YOUR HANDS ON YOUR HEADS AND TAKE ME TO YOUR LEADER.

JERUSALEM! MISTER, GO EASY WITH THAT THING.

YOU THINK HE REALLY WOULD LEGGO OF THE LEVER ON THAT GRENADE?

SLIM, I AIN'T TAKING A CHANCE ON THE KIND OF NUTCASE WHO'LL COME WALKING IN ON US LIKE HE DID

HEY — LIMEY! I AM COMMANDANT OF THIS STOCKADE AND I'M LOCKED IN HERE WITH MY STAFF. I WANT TO KNOW WHAT'S GOING ON.

THAT IS WHAT I AM HERE TO FIND OUT, SIR. PLEASE EXCUSE ME.

WHY YOU BOYS GOT YOUR HANDS LIKE THAT?

IT'S THIS CRAZY LIMEY, MAC. HE'S HOLDING A PINEAPPLE WITH THE PIN OUT.

BOYS, THE JERK IS BLUFFING AND THE ONLY WAY TO HANDLE A BLUFF IS TO CALL IT. JUST WATCH ME.

62

THE END

65

Jay had received a telephone call . . .

A THOUSAND DOLLARS CASH AND ANOTHER FIFTY TO HIRE A PUNT! I LET YOU KNOW HE WAS HERE!

MISTER HICKLEY, YOU'LL GET PAID SOON AS I'VE CHECKED OUT YOUR INFORMATION.

I DO NOT TRUST THAT MAN. HE'S MOST LIKELY BEING PAID BY GELBER FOR A HIDEOUT AND SUPPLIES.

THIS IS THE SIDE-CHANNEL HICKLEY ADVISED USING TO AVOID THE FRONT DOOR.

THAT'S THE SHACK!

AND THAT'S GELBER, BAIL-JUMPER FROM A CHARGE OF BANK ROBBERY.

HUH! WHAT THE HECK?

A SMOKE GRENADE!

66

YOU ARE DONE FOR, BOUNTYMAN. OLD HICKLEY WARNED ME ABOUT THIS BOGHOLE. BIG ENOUGH TO SWALLOW A MULE, HE SAYS. ALL I HAVE TO DO IS WATCH TILL YOU DISAPPEAR!

ONLY THAT STILL LEAVES ME WEARING THESE WRIST-IRONS — SO I'M GIVING YOU A CHANCE! GRAB MY LEGS!

THANKS!

MISTER, YOU OWE ME MORE THAN THANKS FOR SAVING YOUR HIDE.

STILL GOING FOR THE MONEY, HUH? YOU SURE HAVE A ONE-TRACK MIND.

SO I'VE BEEN TOLD.

YUP, THE MONEY'S HERE — EVIDENCE OF YOUR PART IN THAT BANK JOB! YOU WON'T GET AWAY WITH IT LIKE YOU DID WITH THOSE TWO EARLIER ROBBERIES.

YOU COULD AT LEAST TAKE OFF THESE HANDCUFFS AFTER ME PULLING YOU OUT OF THAT MUDHOLE.

AFTER FIRST GETTING ME INTO IT, NO, THOSE BRACELETS STAY ON YOU.

SO YOU BLEW THE WHISTLE ON ME, HUH? WASN'T I PAYING YOU ENOUGH?

BUSTER, I DON'T KNOW WHAT YOU ARE TALKING ABOUT. I JUST DONE MY DUTY LIKE AN HONEST CITIZEN.

THAT AUTOMOBILE AGAIN — THE ONE THAT'S BEEN FOLLOWING ME.

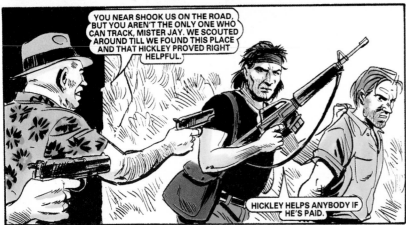

YOU NEAR SHOOK US ON THE ROAD, BUT YOU AREN'T THE ONLY ONE WHO CAN TRACK, MISTER JAY. WE SCOUTED AROUND TILL WE FOUND THIS PLACE AND THAT HICKLEY PROVED RIGHT HELPFUL.

HICKLEY HELPS ANYBODY IF HE'S PAID.

I'LL TAKE YOUR PISTOL AND RIFLE.

THAT IS MY BOY JOHN, MISTER JAY. I DID HAVE ANOTHER SON, BUT HE WAS SHOT BY THIS VARMINT GELBER WHEN HE ROBBED THE BANK AT WHITE PLAIN.

I WAS CLEARED OF THAT JOB, KRAVIT! THE CASE AGAINST ME WAS DROPPED.

FOR LACK OF EVIDENCE — ONLY ME AND JOHN HAVE ALL THE EVIDENCE WE NEED. THAT'S WHY WE USED MISTER JAY TO LEAD US TO YOU. NOW WE AIM TO FIND A QUIET PLACE AND HANG YOU.

JAY, THEY'RE GOING TO MURDER ME. YOU GOTTA STOP THEM. YOU OWE ME, JAY.

YES, I OWE YOU.

ARGH! HE HAD A GUN IN HIS CAR!

MY BOY JOHN! YOU SHOT HIM!

I COULD HAVE DONE, BUT ALL I GAVE HIM WAS A NUMB HAND. DROP YOUR PISTOL AND DON'T MAKE ME DO ANY SERIOUS SHOOTING.

LIKE YOU SAY, GELBER — I OWE YOU! SO I'M PAYING WHAT I THINK IT'S WORTH. I AM GIVING YOU A ONE HOUR START AND THEN I AM COMING AFTER YOU.

JAY, WHAT ABOUT MY MONEY? DON'T I EVEN GET A GUN?

YOU GET NOTHING THAT WILL SLOW YOU DOWN. SO START RUNNING.

AFRAID YOU GENTS HAVE TO BE SECURED TO STOP YOU INTERFERING. THAT GOES FOR YOU TOO, HICKLEY.

HUH — ME?

THAT'S HIS HOUR UP! TIME FOR ME TO GO, GENTS. HOPE YOU AREN'T UNCOMFORTABLE, BUT I'LL FREE YOU WHEN I GET BACK.

EASY TRAIL TO FOLLOW. HE SURE IS TAKING A STRAIGHT LINE FOR A GUY WITH SUCH A TWISTED MIND.

JAY STILL HAS TO GET HIS PRISONER TO AUSTIN IF HE CATCHES HIM. WE STILL HAVE A CHANCE AT HIM.

AW, NO, YOU HAD YOUR CHANCE!

THE END

71

Power boat racing is a rough, tough sport full of thrills and spills. These photographs show you just how tough it can sometimes be.

DO IT ALL

WHSMITH

Arai

TEAM Johnson

A flying start as three boats power away from the line, neck and neck.

THRILLS

Even with a huge hole in his pontoon, this driver is going full out!

What a pile up! This crash occurred at over 100 m.p.h. The drivers were taken to hospital but were found to be only badly bruised.

486

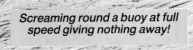

Screaming round a buoy at full speed giving nothing away!

AND SPILLS

Believe it or not this is a cross-channel ferry! The passenger paid £10 for the privilege and thrill of crossing to France in record time.

This shot was caught seconds before the boat went over on its back.

Yes, this pic IS the right way up! The boat has gone over and the driver clings on. He escaped with only bruises.

AAAANGHEEEEEE!

Deep in the South American rain forest a bunch of ranchers were intent on wiping out the indians — and no one seemed to be interested!

Then one day a stranger arrived in the forest . . .

LOOK OUT!

JUMP JETS

EXTERMINATE THE PIGS!

X-BOW

JUST IN TIME!

G . . . GRACIAS, SENOR!

IDIOTS, THESE PEONS! I KEEP WARNING THEM! WHO ARE YOU?

THE NAME'S X-BOW.

The rancher, Roberto Anandez, invited X-Bow to stay the night . . .

TELEPHONE, SENOR ANANDEZ!

EXCUSE ME!

BEWARE X-BOW, ROBERTO! HE'S BEEN HIRED TO INVESTIGATE ATTACKS ON THE KAYAPITO INDIANS.

SO, ANOTHER GOODY-GOODY WANTING TO STOP ME EXTERMINATING THE INDIAN VERMIN. I'LL DEAL WITH HIM!

That night —

THIS WILL HEAT UP THE STRANGER!

X-Bow had expected an attack and was prepared . . .

A MOLOTOV COCKTAIL! THESE GUYS PLAY FOR KEEPS!

MY SPECIAL FIREPROOF GEAR WILL SAVE ME!

HE'S ESCAPED — BUT I'LL GET HIM NOW!

SO, WHITE MAN, SCOUTING FOR MORE VILLAGES TO BURN! YOU SHALL DIE LIKE A DOG ... AS OUR PEACE-LOVING NEIGHBOURS DIED!

THE KAYAPITO ARE COWARDS THEN — IF THEY'D LET A MAN DIE WITHOUT A CHANCE TO DEFEND HIMSELF!

X-Bow knew that the Kayapito were famed as archers ...

I AM THE FINEST ARCHER IN THE WORLD!

YOU INSULT KAYTINO! I CHALLENGE YOU. I FINEST ARCHER!

A DUEL TO THE DEATH! FIRE WHEN YOU LIKE!

THEIR ARROWS ARE POISONED. ONE MISTAKE AND I'M DEAD.

AAIEE! HE HAS HIT THE ARROW!

YOU ARE NO ORDINARY MAN.

NO, I'M X-BOW AND YOUR FRIEND. I COME TO HELP YOU FIGHT THOSE WHO ARE TRYING TO EXTERMINATE YOU.

NOW A MESH BOLT SHOULD DO THE TRICK.

WE THANK YOU. OLD GODS SAY IF FOREST BURN MOTHER EARTH DIE OF FEVER.

OUR SCIENTISTS SAY THE SAME THING. BUT WE SHALL NOT LET IT HAPPEN.

X-Bow reckoned that Kaytino's village would be next to be attacked so ...

MAN WITH PATCH OVER EYE DESTROY INDIANS.

JUST AS I SUSPECTED. BUT THIS TIME HE'LL GET A SHOCK! HERE'S WHAT WE DO ...

78

Two days later . . .

LOOKS LIKE THE VERMIN HAVE FLED, SENOR ANANDEZ.

PITY! THERE'S NOTHING I LIKE BETTER THAN ROASTING THEM OUT! WHAT'S THIS THING — SOME KIND OF RAMP?

SOME HEATHENISH NONSENSE . . . BURN IT DOWN WITH THE REST!

THIS TIME YOU'LL GET YOUR MURDERING FINGERS BURNED, ANANDEZ!

X-BOW! I THOUGHT WE'D SCARED HIM OFF.

MULTI EXTINGUISHER BOLTS GONE! THE CHEMICAL WILL PUT OUT THEIR TORCHES!

KILL HIM!

THE INDIANS! WHERE DID THEY SPRING FROM! UGH!

DUUNGH!

79

NO! ENOUGH WILD GOOSE-CHASING! I AM STOPPING THIS STORY — NOW! WE ARE RETURNING TO LONDON!

Then on a quiet stretch of road . . .

SORRY ABOUT THIS. CAB'S ACTING A BIT ODD. I'D BETTER MAKE A CALL FROM THAT HOUSE BACK THERE — GET ANOTHER CAB OUT TO YOU.

OH, NO! THAT JUST ABOUT MAKES MY DAY! AN IDIOT REPORTER AND NOW A BROKEN-DOWN CAB!

SOMETHING'S NOT RIGHT!

WHY DIDN'T HE STOP OUTSIDE THE HOUSE? AND IT'S ODD FOR A CAB TO BREAK DOWN. THEY'RE USUALLY CHECKED OVER THOROUGHLY BEFORE HITTING THE ROAD. I DON'T LIKE THIS! I'LL FOLLOW HIM!

WE'LL BE LUCKY TO GET A FLIGHT OUT TODAY AT THIS RATE. AND WHERE ARE YOU GOING?

HE — HE'S TAKING OFF ON THAT MOTOR-CYCLE! IT WAS A SET-UP! BUT WHY? WHAT CAN — OH, NO! IT CAN MEAN ONLY ONE THING. I'D BETTER DO A QUICK CHANGE — AND NOW!

OUT, WOMAN! OUT OF THE CAR!

KING COBRA! AGAIN!

WHAT ON EARTH? I CAN —

ARE YOU DEAF, LADY? I SAID OUT! AND THAT MEANS NOW!

THE CAR'S BLOWN UP!

HERE'S A CHANCE TO MAKE SURE SHE SANCTIONS THE TANGIER'S TRIP.

THIS IS NO GAME FOR YOU TWO. ESPECIALLY YOU — A WOMAN. PERSUADE BILL KING TO TAKE YOU BACK TO LONDON. AND IF HE'S GOT ANY FANCY IDEAS ABOUT HEADING INTO THE WASPS' NEST IN TANGIER, TELL HIM TO FORGET IT!

FORGET IT? WE'LL SHOW HIM!

When Bill King returned suitably startled . . .

I THOUGHT I HEARD — W-WHAT HAPPENED? THE CAB!

SHUT UP, KING! JUST SHUT UP! GET US TO THAT AIRPORT! WE'RE GOING TO TANGIER!

Later on the plane to Tangier . . .

WELL, NOW! THAT LITTLE BIT OF PSYCHOLOGY WORKED! THIS TRIP TO MOROCCO MIGHT BE A WASTE OF TIME, BUT AT LEAST WE'RE GOING!

WHAT ARE YOU GRINNING AT, KING?

OH! ER — JUST THINKING . . . ALL WE HAVE TO DO IS MAKE A CALL TO KOMMISSAR BRAND TO PICK UP THE CLERK AT THAT HOTEL IN COPENHAGEN. HE'S THE ONLY ONE WHO COULD'VE KNOWN WHERE WE WERE HEADING. THAT OUGHT TO CLEAN UP THE DANISH END!

At Tangier . . .

TAXI! TAXI! YOU WANT TAXI — CHEAP!

WELL, MA'AM, TAKE YOUR PICK!

NO MORE CABS, KING. THIS TIME WE HIRE A CAR, AND CHOOSE OUR OWN!

HERTZ

MY, MY! MS KERRIGAN! THINK OF THE EXPENSE!

SMIRK AWAY, BILL KING. YOUR TIME WITH INTERNATIONAL NEWS GROUP IS FAST RUNNING OUT!

YOUR MALE PRIDE MAY BE HURT, MR KING, BUT I FEEL A LOT SAFER IF I'M AT THE WHEEL.

OKAY, MA'AM. BUT I HOPE YOU KNOW HOW TO SHAKE A TAIL, BECAUSE THAT'S WHAT WE'VE GOT. THAT BLACK SALOON HAS BEEN WITH US SINCE WE LEFT THE AIRPORT!

BETTER LET ME DRIVE! I KNOW TANGIER AND YOU DON'T! WE COULD END UP CORNERED IN SOME BACK ALLEY.

YOU'RE JUST TRYING TO SCARE ME AGAIN, KING. HOW COULD IT BE A TAIL? WHO KNOWS WE'RE HERE?

THAT DESK CLERK AT THE HOTEL KNEW FOR STARTERS, LADY! NOW LET ME DRIVE! YOU SHOULD HAVE STUCK TO THE AVENUE D'ESPAGNE. YOU'LL GET US SNARLED UP IN THE CASBAH FOR SURE!

Y-YOU'RE RIGHT, KING! THEY ARE FOLLOWING US! WHERE ARE WE? WHERE DO I TURN NOW?

WE'RE HEADING FOR THE KASBAH'EN, LADY. THE OLD TOWN RISES TO A KIND OF SUMMIT — A DEAD-END. BRACE YOURSELF FOR TROUBLE!

OH, NO! IF YOU SAY 'I TOLD YOU SO', I'LL SCREAM!

SAVE YOUR SCREAMING, MA'AM — YOU'RE GOING TO NEED IT!

K-KING . . . D-DON'T GET OUT! WE — WE CAN STAY HERE AND LOCK THE DOORS!

SURE. THEN ALL THEY'LL DO IS SPRAY THE CAR WITH BULLETS AND SHOVE IT OVER THE EDGE.

MOVE IT, IDIOT! RUN HIM DOWN!

CAN'T SEE! HE'S BLOCKING THE VIEW!

NOOOO! AIEEEEE!

VERY SUITABLE! RIGHT INTO THE COMMUNAL RUBBISH-TIP!

I WARNED YOU, LADY! LIKE I SAID — LEAVE THIS TO ME! I'D BETTER GO TAKE A LOOK AT YOUR REPORTER PAL. MAYBE HE WASN'T SO LUCKY...

By the time Bill King reappeared, Jill Kerrigan had recovered her self-assurance...

Y-YOU OKAY, MS KERRIGAN? I — I WAS KNOCKED OUT FOR A WHILE THERE!

THINK NOTHING OF IT, BILL KING! I'M GETTING USED TO YOU VANISHING WHEN THE GOING GETS TOUGH...

...JUST BEFORE KING COBRA APPEARS? I WONDER?

WE'D BETTER FIND THE HOTEL. I NEED TO CHANGE... A BATH...

YOU'RE NOT GETTING IN THAT CAR WITH ME, KING! YOU STINK — IN MORE WAYS THAN ONE!

HEY! WHAT'S THIS?

YOU FIND A CAB! I'LL SEE YOU LATER.

PERFECT! THIS GIVES ME A CHANCE TO ACT ON MY OWN. I CAN GET AROUND A LOT FASTER AS KING COBRA. AND I'M CLEARLY ON THE RIGHT TRACK FROM THIS WASPS' NEST I'VE STIRRED UP!

BILL KING'S THE NAME. I HAVE A ROOM BOOKED...

After a shower...

SO OUR JILLIE HASN'T BOOKED IN YET. GUESS SHE WENT STRAIGHT TO THE PRESSING PLANT. SO HERE GOES —

THERE IT IS AND SHE'S JUST ARRIVED. I THINK I'D BETTER TAKE A QUICK LOOK AROUND.

CLASSICAL RECORDS

CLASSICAL RECORDS

NOW — LET'S LOWER MY SPECIAL MIKE TO SEE WHAT WE CAN PICK UP! I'D GUESS THE PLACE IS BUZZING OVER JILL'S ARRIVAL. IF THESE GUYS ARE CROOKED, THEN THEY'LL HAVE ASSUMED US BOTH DEAD BY NOW!

MAIN OFFICE

SOMETHING'S GONE WRONG. THAT WOMAN'S HERE AT THE GATE — RIGHT NOW!

THE ORDERS FROM LONDON WERE TO DESTROY No.3 SECTION IF WE COULDN'T REMOVE THEM. SO — WE CAN DO BOTH. WE CAN DESTROY IT AND HER.

No 3 SECTION SPECIAL PRESSING KEEP OUT

I WONDER WHAT IS SO 'SPECIAL' ABOUT THOSE PRESSINGS? I'D BEST TAKE A LOOK INSIDE!

I'D BETTER TAKE A LOOK AT No.3 SECTION!

HMM! NOT VERY PROMISING! JUST STACKS OF RECORDS ALL READY FOR PACKING AND SHIPPING! MAYBE I'D BETTER TAKE A CLOSER LOOK — BUT AS BILL KING, JUST IN CASE SOMEONE WALKS THROUGH THAT OTHER DOOR.

BIZET

CARMEN →

THE PEARL FISHERS ←

L'ARLESIENNE FAIRMAID OF PERTH ←
BY PLACIDO DOMINGO

PRESSING

JUST WHAT THE LABEL SAYS — A RECORD OF BIZET'S CARMEN! SO, WHAT'S SO 'SPECIAL' ABOUT THIS? I DON'T GET IT! MAYBE I SHOULD TAKE A LOOK INSIDE THAT 'PRESSING' ROOM . . .

But before he could move . . .

Meanwhile . . .

WE ARE DELIGHTED THAT YOU ARE TAKING SUCH AN INTEREST IN OUR LITTLE CONCERN.

NOT SO LITTLE, MR HASSAN. IT'S A WORLD-WIDE ORGANISATION. I MYSELF AM A MEMBER OF THE CLASSICAL RECORD CLUB! YOU HAVE A DISTINGUISHED MANAGING DIRECTOR IN SIR HENRY PACKHAM . . .

HERE, WE HAVE A VERY SPECIAL SECTION WHICH YOU MUST SEE . . .

SECTION 3

WHAT'S SO SPECIAL ABOUT IT?

YOU'LL NEVER KNOW, MISS NOSEY-PARKER! YOU'LL NEVER KNOW!

NOW!

WHA — I MMMMPH!

Some time later . . .

OOOOH! WH-WHAT HAPPENED . . . WHERE AM I? AND WH-WHO'S THERE? I — I CAN HEAR BREATHING! WHO IS IT?

OH, NO! JILL KERRIGAN! THEY'VE GOT HER TOO! NOW WHAT DO I DO? I'M TRUSSED UP LIKE A CHICKEN — AND I CAN'T CHANGE INTO KING COBRA. OH, BOY! FROM WHAT THOSE ARABS WERE SAYING EARLIER, THIS PLACE IS GOING TO BLOW SKY-HIGH AT ANY MINUTE . . .

CONTINUED ON PAGE 113.

Minutes later . . .

IT'S COOLED HIM DOWN, THOUGH! HE AIN'T SO KEEN TO CROCK OLE CROCODILE NOW!

ONE ALL! THAT'S BETTER!

GREAT GOAL, CROCODILE!

In the second-half . . .

ON YER GO, KID!

YES, IT'S THERE! TWO ONE!

GOOD ON YER, LAD! THAT'S A BEAUT!

After the game . . .

WE DID IT! MAYBE WE DID NEED SOMEBODY LIKE YOU, CROCODILE. THOUGHT WE'D NEVER WIN AGAIN!

WELL, JUST GOES TO SHOW!

That evening . . .

YOBS! THIS SYDNEY FELLER CALLS US YOBS!

DREBTON BUGLE TOPS FOR SPORT

AUSSIE THUG LEADS UNITED YOBS!

— SYDNEY COLEMAN

COLEMAN'S ALWAYS HAD A DOWN ON US.

91

KIDNAPPED TWO PEACE-LOVING BRITISH CITIZENS AND CAUSED A BREACH OF THE PEACE. THE MAN'S A MENACE. I WANT HIM ARRESTED!

YER, ME TOO!

MATT McGHEE! WE'D LIKE YOU TO COME WITH US. WE'VE HAD A PHONE CALL ABOUT YOU!

WOT? FOR TEACHING CHOOKS SOME MANNERS?

YOU'LL APPEAR IN COURT ON MONDAY. IF YOU'RE FOUND GUILTY, YOU COULD LOSE YOUR WORK PERMIT AND BE DEPORTED. MEANTIME BE ON YOUR BEST BEHAVIOUR.

AT LEAST I'LL BE ABLE TO PLAY IN SATURDAY'S GAME.

On Friday, Dregton travelled to Charworth for the next day's match against Hotspur, the league leaders. Defeat meant relegation!

I WANT EVERYBODY IN BED BY TEN. NO SLIPPIN' OUT ON THE TOWN.

RIGHT, CROCODILE.

But that night . . .

COUPLA HOURS AT A NIGHTCLUB WON'T MAKE ANY DIFFERENCE.

I GOTTA CLAMP DOWN ON THIS!

Half-an-hour later . . .

THIS IS THE LIFE!

Then Hotspur got a corner and . . .

Matt's vision cleared . . .

Matt got unsteadily to his feet and . . .

THE POACHER

NORMANDY, D-DAY, 6th JUNE 1944! The Allies returned in force to drive the Germans out of the occupied countries of Europe.

Sam "Poacher" Watts and Jacko Jackson, sniper-scouts, landed with their glider regiment . . .

RIGHT, SAM, WE KNOW WHAT TO DO. WE'VE TO MOVE FORWARD AND COVER THE APPROACH ROAD.

I'M RIGHT WITH YOU, JACKO!

They were soon in position . . .

I HEAR ENGINE NOISE.

YEAH, MATE! HERE THEY COME!

A TANK WITH SOME SUPPORT TROOPS! WE'LL SLOW THEM UP!

AARGH!

SOON HAVE YOU BACK!

NICE WORK, POACHER! YOU'LL FIND A DRESSING STATION SET UP IN THE BARN NEAR THE BRIDGE.

FIRE WHEN READY, NUMBER ONE.

THAT'LL HOLD THEM UP FOR A WHILE.

THANKS, MATE. LISTEN — ER, I'M NOT TALKING ABOUT YOU FREEZING OUT THERE.

MAYBE YOU AIN'T — BUT I HAVE TO.

COULDN'T DO IT, SIR! I JUST COULDN'T SQUEEZE THAT TRIGGER AND KILL A MAN. SORRY, SIR. YOU KNOW I'VE ALWAYS DONE MY BEST.

NO MAN CAN DO MORE THAN HIS BEST. I'M AFRAID IT HAS TO BE THE COOKHOUSE FOR YOU WHILE I THINK THIS OVER.

Poacher Sam settled in to his new duties . . .

BUNNIES IS FINE FOR COMPO STEW, BUT WHAT I'D LIKE IS SOME NICE FRESH CHICKENS.

I RECKON THERE ISN'T A HEN LEFT IN THIS PART OF FRANCE. STILL, I'LL SEE WHAT I CAN DO.

99

Sam resumed his old trade . . .

ALWAYS KNEW I COULD FIND A PHEASANT OR TWO!

PHEASANT WITH THE COMPO RATIONS!

IT'S WHAT YOU MIGHT CALL A LITTLE EXTRA, SIR. COURTESY OF PRIVATE WATTS!

Sam was summoned . . .

SO IGNORING OUR OUTPOSTS AND JERRIES, YOU TODDLE OUT AT NIGHT TO ENJOY A LITTLE HUNTING.

SORT OF, SIR. SORRY IF THE PHEASANT'S A BIT GAMEY, BUT IT DID OUGHT TO BE HUNG A FEW DAYS.

YOU — YOU — ER, YES, SARN'T-MAJOR! WHAT IS IT?

CODEWORD JUNIPER'S JUST COME OVER THE RADIO FROM THE BEACH-HEAD, SIR. IT MEANS THE JOCKS ARE BREAKING OUT TO LINK WITH US.

THAT COULD BE WHY JERRY'S BEEN QUIET FOR THE PAST FEW HOURS.

NO POINT WAITING TO BE DISMISSED NOW THE MAJOR'S GOT OTHER THINGS ON HIS MIND.

At dawn a recce patrol reported . . .

WE WENT RIGHT THROUGH TO THE CROSSROADS WITHOUT SEEING A SIGN OF JERRY, SIR.

HE MUST HAVE HEARD ABOUT THE JOCKS AND BE TRYING TO STOP THEM! WE'LL TRY AND ADVANCE TO THE VILLAGE!

WHAT THE —

JUST THE CORPORAL-COOK FISHING WITH A GRENADE, SIR.

QUICKER THAN NETTING 'EM, EH, POACHER!

IT MAY BE, BUT IT RUINS THE FISH. THEY DON'T KEEP AND THEY TASTE HORRIBLE.

HOOK-AND-LINING IS THE BEST WAY. HUM! SHOULD BE EASY TO SLIP ALONG UPRIVER NOW THE GERMANS HAVE PULLED OUT.

Sam slipped away . . .

Sam crept forward . . .

JERRY HALF-TRACKS! I WONDER WHAT ELSE IS HERE!

THE TYRE PRINTS WEREN'T HERE TWO NIGHTS AGO. WHY ARE THEY HERE NOW IF JERRY WAS PULLING OUT LAST NIGHT? I'D BEST FOLLOW THEM!

A single rifle fired . . .

Poacher Sam did it again and again . . .

103

When she goes to sea, H.M.S. Ark Royal has a complement of almost 1000 men. This means that as well as her fighting capability she must also provide all the services, laundry, baking etc., that are needed in a small town. These pics show just some of the multitude of tasks that are done on this mighty ship.

Just like the shop in a small town the N.A.A.F.I. sells all that a sailor might need.

A mechanic works on the tail section of a Sea Harrier.

Ready to enter harbour. The crew man the ship on arrival at Malta.

The Mighty Ark

On the bridge. From here all the ship's movements are directed.

Time for some relaxation in a game of deck hockey.

In the galley, where everything from pizzas to elaborate cakes etc. is prepared.

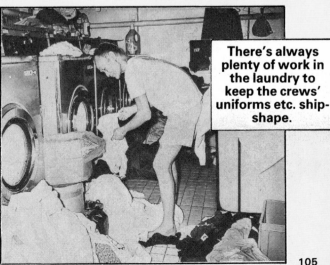

There's always plenty of work in the laundry to keep the crews' uniforms etc. ship-shape.

Crewmen work on a Vulcan Phalanx gun which is effective even against Exocet missiles.

SERGEANT

CONTINUED FROM PAGE 48.

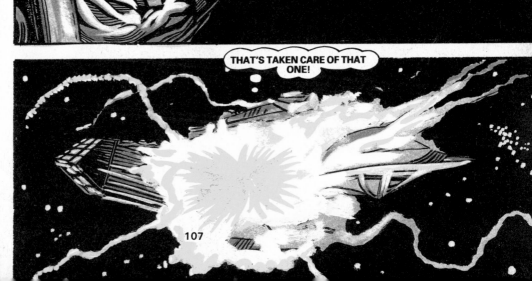

IT'S BLOWN UP! THAT'LL TEACH THEM TO ATTACK INNOCENT WAYFARERS!

THAT'S NUMBER TWO!

THE LAST ONE'S FLED! THEY'LL THINK TWICE NEXT TIME.

Meanwhile at Scum City . . .

THAT CHAIN, MY FRIEND, I SHALL HAVE IT BACK — IT IS MINE!

YOURS MONK? YOU'D BETTER COME AND TAKE IT! MORGA THE PIRATE GAVE IT TO ME ON HIS DEATH BED.

YOU MUST DIE THEN, LOUIS LAVAL.

NOTHING STOPS HIM!

DIE!

108

LAVAL IS DEAD! I, DEATH MAN, SHALL TAKE OVER SCUM CITY! NONE CAN STOP ME FOR I CANNOT BE KILLED. OPPOSE ME AND I SHALL DESTROY YOUR CITY!

WE . . . WE AGREE!

Sixty continued on his journey . . .

ROCK STORM AHEAD AND MY FORCE FIELD GENERATORS WERE DAMAGED IN THE BATTLE! I'VE ONLY A FLIMSY WALL SHIELD BETWEEN ME AND DEATH . . .

I'VE GOT TO PRESS ON! IT'D TAKE LIGHT YEARS TO GO ROUND!

THAT ONE'S NOT GOING TO MISS!

GOT IT!

THROUGH AT LAST AND THERE'S ZUR AHEAD!

Sixty landed . . .

THE PLANT'S IN ABUNDANCE! IT WON'T TAKE ME LONG TO GATHER WHAT I NEED!

GAAAAAAARGH!

G . . . GREAT SPINNING SATELLITES!

I CAN'T STOP IT! ITS HEAD IS TOO WELL PROTECTED!

BUT THE LEGS AREN'T PROTECTED AT ALL.

PHEW! IT ALMOST SKEWERED ME.

. . . BUT THAT'S FINISHED IT!

LET'S HOPE I'M NOT TOO LATE TO SAVE BEN AND THE OTHERS!

110

Immediately Sixty returned, a serum was made from the plants and given to the victims . .

I HOPE I'M NOT TOO LATE!

HE ISN'T AS FAR GONE AS THE OTHERS. PERHAPS BECAUSE HE HAD HIS SPACE SUIT ON WHEN DEATH MAN TOUCHED HIM.

Two hours later . . .

WE'RE ALL ON THE MEND, SARGE! WE CAN'T THANK YOU ENOUGH.

THAT WAS ONLY PART OF MY TASK, BEN! I MUST PUT AN END TO DEATH MAN BEFORE HE STRIKES AGAIN!

DEATH MAN SEEMS TO ENJOY THE MOCK ROMAN GAMES. I SHALL CHALLENGE HIM ONCE THE CHARIOT RACE IS OVER!

DEATH MAN, I CHALLENGE YOU TO BATTLE! I COME TO RID THE UNIVERSE OF YOUR EVIL!

WATCH! HE SHALL WITHER AND DIE LIKE ALL THE OTHERS!

MY MONEY'S ON DEATH MAN!

I WISH SIXTY'D SEE HIM OFF, THOUGH. I HATE HIM!

DIE, SIXTY! IT'S STRANGE HOW SOME VICTIMS ARE SO HELPLESS IN MY POWER. LIKE THE SPIDER AND THE FLY.

SOON THE SKIN WILL WITHER AWAY!

THE END

KING COBRA

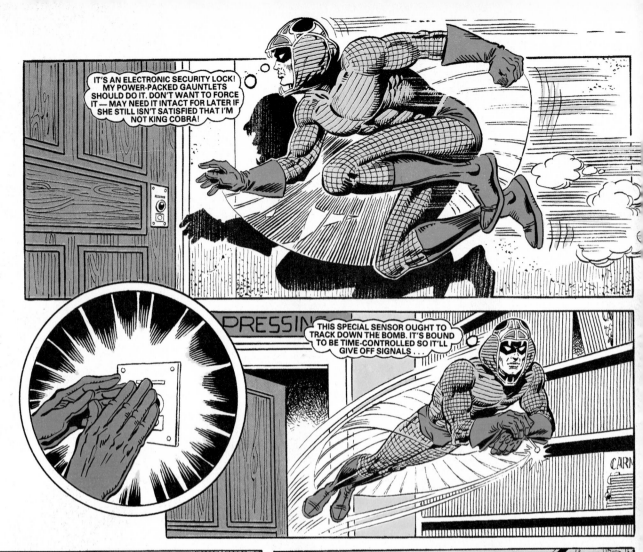

IT'S AN ELECTRONIC SECURITY LOCK! MY POWER-PACKED GAUNTLETS SHOULD DO IT. DON'T WANT TO FORCE IT — MAY NEED IT INTACT FOR LATER IF SHE STILL ISN'T SATISFIED THAT I'M NOT KING COBRA!

THIS SPECIAL SENSOR OUGHT TO TRACK DOWN THE BOMB. IT'S BOUND TO BE TIME-CONTROLLED SO IT'LL GIVE OFF SIGNALS . . .

THERE'S THE LITTLE BABY! AND FROM THAT CLOCK-FACE I DON'T HAVE TIME FOR ANY FANCY DE-FUSING! JUST TIME ENOUGH TO GET IT OUT OF HERE!

I CAN JUST HEAVE THE THING CLEAR. THE PLACE IS DESERTED ANYWAY! THEY'LL ALL HAVE FLOWN THE COOP BY NOW!

THERE SHE GOES! WHAT — OH, NOOO! JILL KERRIGAN — AND SHE'S RUNNING STRAIGHT FOR THE DEVICE!

THAT GIRL HAS A KNACK FOR RUNNING STRAIGHT INTO TROUBLE AND GIVING ME HEADACHES!

EEEEEK!

DOWN!!

YOU AGAIN! AND DEAR BILL KING IS ONCE MORE CONVENIENTLY OUT OF THE WAY! THIS TIME I'VE GOT YOU, PAL! YOU'RE COMING WITH ME . . . I WANT TO SEE YOU BOTH FACE-TO-FACE IF IT'S AT ALL POSSIBLE WITH ONE MAN!

I'VE NO IDEA WHAT YOU'RE YAPPING ABOUT, LADY. BUT IF YOU KNOW WHERE YOUR REPORTER BOY-FRIEND IS, THEN IT SAVES ME A JOB. I'VE WORK TO DO!

NOW I HAVE TO MOVE REALLY FAST!

HUH! I'M STILL NOT CONVINCED. BUT BILL KING CAN'T BE IN TWO PLACES AT ONCE, SO . . .

IF HE'S COBRA, THEN HE'LL HAVE HAD TO BUST HIS WAY OUT OF THAT ROOM! IF NOT, HE'LL STILL BE SAFELY LOCKED-UP IN THERE!

JILL KERRIGAN IS A PAIN IN THE NECK! BUT FOR HER I COULD BE HOT-FOOTING IT AFTER THOSE VILLAINS INSTEAD OF PLAYING HIDE AND SEEK! THANK THE STARS I HAD THE SENSE TO LEAVE THAT LOCK INTACT!

BIZET

PRESSING

CARMEN

THE PEARL

Panel 1: IT'S STILL LOCKED! AND IT LOOKS LIKE A TIME-LOCK! BUT IT'S SET TO OPEN IN TWO MINUTES — CLEVER! RIGHT AFTER THE EXPLOSION! IF BILL KING IS STILL IN THERE, THEN THIS CLEARS HIM OKAY!

Panel 2: MISS KERRIGAN! THANK GOODNESS! NOW — LET'S GO — THEY COULD HAVE SET A BOMB — A FIRE — ANYTHING. WE MUST —

RELAX! IT'S ALL BEEN HANDLED — BY KING COBRA! YOU CAN STOP SHAKING, CHICKEN-LIVER! AND TO THINK I SUSPECTED . . .

Panel 3: WELL, WE'RE LUCKY! WE CAN TAKE ALL THE TIME WE NEED TO REALLY GO THROUGH THIS PLACE WITH A FINE-TOOTH COMB. SEE JUST WHAT IT WAS THEY WERE TRYING TO COVER-UP.

MY, MY! AT LEAST YOUR BRAIN DIDN'T FREEZE-UP WITH FEAR, KING. YOU CAN STILL ADD TWO-AND-TWO . . .

Panel 4: Two hours later . . .

NOTHING! A BIG FAT NOTHING! JUST RECORDS! IT DOESN'T MAKE SENSE, KING!

WHY? WHY TRY TO BLOW THE PLACE UP IF THERE'S NOTHING TO HIDE? WHAT'S SO SPECIAL ABOUT HUNDREDS OF RECORDS OF BIZET'S MUSIC THAT THEY WANTED TO DESTROY THEM? LET'S GET BACK TO THE HOTEL!

Panel 5: ER — LOOK, BILL, I WANT TO FRESHEN UP. CAN YOU SLIP INTO THE DINING-ROOM AND BOOK US A TABLE FOR LUNCH?

IN THE HOTEL? WHAT ABOUT THAT EXPENSE-ACCOUNT, MS KERRIGAN? WOULDN'T A LOCAL CAFE BE BETTER?

SHE'S TRYING TO DITCH ME FOR SOME REASON . . .

Panel 6:

MR KING ASKED ME TO CHECK ON HIS MAIL. HAVE YOU ANYTHING?

NO, MA'AM. NOTHING FOR MR KING . . .

WHAT THE — ? AGAIN SHE'S CHECKING ON MY MAIL! WHAT'S GOING ON? CAN SHE BE INVOLVED IN THIS RACKET SOMEHOW? SHE'LL BEAR WATCHING . . .

Panel 7: Over lunch . . .

YOU SAID YOU WERE A MEMBER OF THAT RECORD CLUB. WHAT'S THE ROUTINE — SAME AS A BOOK CLUB? YOU GET A LIST OF RECORDS AND JUST ORDER BY POST?

RIGHT! I HAVE THIS MONTH'S CATALOGUE WITH ME, ACTUALLY. TAKE A LOOK — NOTHING SUSPICIOUS ABOUT IT AT ALL . . .

CLASSICAL RECORD CLUB

Panel 8:

THEY'RE ALIVE! SOMETHING WENT WRONG!

ALLAH! THANKS FOR CALLING! I'LL GET SOMEONE ON IT NOW!

ODD!

WHAT'S ODD?

NO MENTION OF BIZET AT ALL! YET WE SIFTED THROUGH HUNDREDS OF 'EM.

BUSY. NEXT OUT ... BUSY ... IT'S ALL ...

BIZET IS PRONOUNCED THE SAME WAY AS BUSY — NEAR ENOUGH. COULD THAT BE WHAT HE WAS TALKING ABOUT! NEXT OUT ... BIZET?

HAVE YOU FINALLY FLIPPED, KING? BUSY — BIZET! WHAT ARE YOU ON ABOUT?

ER — JUST AN IDEA. THERE'S SOMETHING WE'RE MISSING AT THAT PLACE. WE'RE GOING BACK!

HAVE TO WATCH IT. I GOT SO EXCITED I ALMOST BLEW THE GAFF. BILL KING WOULDN'T KNOW THE DYING HANSEN'S LAST WORDS!

Bill drove like a maniac but ...

OH, NO! WE'RE TOO LATE — BUT I'M NOT LETTING THIS GO! I'M GOING IN THERE!

WHAT! ARE YOU CRAZY? THAT PLACE IS AN INFERNO!

I'VE GOT TO RISK IT! LET'S HOPE THIS SMOKE HIDES MY QUICK CHANGE. I MUST TRY TO SAVE ONE OF THOSE RECORDS. THERE IS SOMETHING TIED UP IN THIS BIZET BUSINESS AND I HAVE TO FIND OUT WHAT IT IS!

THERE'S A SLIM CHANCE — IF I'M FAST ENOUGH!

GOT ONE!

After another quick change . . .

TANGIERS TRIP!

DON'T SOUND SO DISAPPOINTED, LADY. LOOK, I BROUGHT YOU A PRESENT —

THAT RECORD IS JUST A RECORD, BILL KING. I DON'T KNOW WHAT YOU'RE HOPING TO PROVE IN THAT FRIEND'S LABORATORY BACK IN LONDON!

JUST A HUNCH, LADY. BUT I THINK YOU'LL BE MORE THAN RELIEVED IF I'M RIGHT!

Bill was right! Some hours later at a lab in London . . .

THE WHOLE DISC IS COMPRESSED HEROIN! IN THAT STATE IT LOOKS ENOUGH LIKE A NORMAL DISC PRESSING TO PASS WITHOUT RAISING AN EYEBROW! NEAT!

THEY COULD SHIP THEM ANYWHERE THEY WANTED UNDER THE COVER OF THE CLASSICAL RECORD CLUB! WHAT A SYSTEM! NOW WE GET IN CONTACT WITH THE CLUB'S CHAIRMAN, SIR HENRY PACKHAM!

Soon—

THAT'S SPLENDID NEWS! COME ALONG AND BRING THAT RECORD WITH YOU!

On the way to Packham's house . . .

OH, DEAR! WONDER WHAT'S WRONG?

STAY IN THE CAR. I'LL CHECK! SOMETHING'S NOT RIGHT.

THE SHOES! GO! DRIVE ON! THEY'RE NOT COPS! KEEP THE APPOINTMENT!

STOP HER!

118

119

AH — JUST A GRAZE. SHE'S COMING TO. TIME FOR COBRA TO DISAPPEAR . . .

It was the end of the line for the Classical Record Club — and the drugs racket. Sir Henry was arrested and told the police all he knew. It would only be a matter of time before all the gang members were behind bars.

Later—

YOU — YOU'VE BEEN OF SOME HELP IN THIS STORY, KING, WE'RE OIL AND WATER — WE JUST DON'T MIX! YOU'RE NOT A BAD REPORTER, YOU'LL GET ANOTHER POSITION EASILY ENOUGH!

WHOAAAA! EASY, LADY . . .

THIS FINALLY CAUGHT-UP WITH ME! NOW I KNOW WHY YOU WERE ALWAYS ASKING FOR MY MAIL AT THE VARIOUS HOTELS. YOU'D ALREADY RENEWED MY CONTRACT FOR ANOTHER FIVE YEARS BEFORE WE ACTUALLY MET.

YOU WANTED TO GET IT BACK AND TEAR IT UP BEFORE I SAW IT. TOO BAD! LOOKS LIKE WE'RE STUCK WITH EACH OTHER FOR A WHILE LONGER, LITTLE LADY!

GET OUT OF HERE, YOU MALE CHAUVINIST . . .

THE END

121

125